The Pardoner

AND OTHER PLAYS

compiled by Irene Yates

Contents

How to Read the Plays

The three plays in this book are for you to read aloud in small groups. Two of the plays have six parts including the narrator. The first play has a seventh part, a chemist, which could be read by one of the other characters, for example, the old man.

Follow the play carefully and when it is your turn to speak, remember to say your part clearly. Try to speak the way your character would talk. If you think your character is loud and bossy then you should read the part in a loud, bossy voice. If you are reading the part of a king or somebody very important, try to convey this in the way you read your lines.

1 Skim through the play and look over your parts.

2 Read your lines quietly to yourself.

3 Read the play aloud in your group.

4 Re-read the play and make sure that you use the right sort of voice for your character.

5 Swap roles and read the part of a different character.

The Pardoner's Tale

A Classic Tale
Adapted by Paul Copley
Illustrations by Holly Swain

Cast

Pardoner
a man who sells pardons

Innkeeper
a jolly landlord of an inn

Old man
a wise and careful man

Chemist
a helpful shopkeeper

Joker   **Jack**   **Ace**
three ruffians

The Pardoner's Tale

Pardoner   *I am a pardoner, this is my tale*
It will make your teeth chatter, make you go pale
It may make you shiver with fear and dread
So leave the light on when you go to bed!

Six hundred and fifty years ago, on the road to Canterbury, there was an inn. It stood at a crossroads and was a very busy place. One night it was full of pilgrims who were on their way to Canterbury Cathedral. The innkeeper was a noisy, jolly person who liked to keep his customers happy.

Scene 1   At the inn

Innkeeper   Yes sir, can I help you?

Old man You are very busy tonight, Innkeeper. Who are all these people?

Innkeeper *There's a cook over there with a sore on his*
knee
A knight with his squire who looks scrawny
to me
A wife from Bath, who is plump and good fun
There's a doctor, a sea captain, even a nun!
And over in the corner under the light
A pardoner sits this very night.

Old man A pardoner?

Innkeeper He sells pardons on sheets of paper. He tells sinners that if they buy them they will be forgiven. I do not believe him.

Pardoner But some people believed that a pardoner could forgive sins. Some people would believe anything! Remember, it was six hundred and fifty years ago, and people needed to hope for better times. This was the time of the Black Death – the Plague!

Innkeeper *They tell me another one's died from the Plague!*

Old man *That's right and I knew her – a dairymaid.*

Innkeeper *It's the year 1350! You'd think they'd have found*
A cure by now! Oops, do not look round!

Old man *Why not? What's the matter? What is to do?*

Innkeeper *It's those three ruffians, they are staring at you!*

Pardoner *In the corner, three gamblers, Ace, Jack and Joker*
Were drinking and playing a card game called poker
They were looking for trouble, but just in time
A church bell rang and they heard its chime!

Joker *Hear that lads? That's the funeral bell*
Sending someone to Heaven or Hell.

Jack *I wonder, who is it? How did they die?*

Ace *Who cares! Fetch more ale, Jack! It's your turn to buy!*

Pardoner	The three hooligans walked over to the innkeeper and pushed the old man out of the way.
Old man	Careful!
Ace	Shut up, old man!
Innkeeper	All right, that's enough. You had all better leave right now.
Joker	We can't do that.
Jack	We are waiting for our friend, Percy.
Old man	Don't bother.
Ace	What?

Old man You won't see Percy again.

Jack Why not?

Innkeeper *Last night your friend Percy was drunk,*
    pie-eyed!
He was lying flat out on the bench outside
When along came a thief by the name of Death
Speared him through the heart, Percy breathed
    his last breath!

Pardoner At first, the three ruffians could not believe
what the innkeeper said. They got angry and
wanted revenge. That was their first mistake!

Ace *You say he's called Death, who stole Percy's life?*

Innkeeper *Yes. We'll all meet him sometime – so says my wife!*

Joker *If ever I meet him, then he'd better watch out! I'll teach him a lesson, without a doubt.*

Old man *Be careful youth! In this plague, Death's near Watch out, he's strong, he's something to fear He's seen off a thousand, he's clever and sly He took a whole family from a village nearby!*

Jack *This village nearby, is that where he lives?*

Innkeeper *I'm not sure if that's the address that he gives.*

Ace *Well, that's where we'll go – come on – no more fuss We'll go and get him before he gets us!*

Joker *Yes – death to this traitor Death! – I'm with you He's taken our friend but he'll not take us two!*

Jack *Hang on count me in, there's three of us here Death may think he's fierce, we'll fill him with fear!*

Innkeeper *Now listen, you're drunk and Death's never been beat By St Mary, you'd best take great care if you meet!*

Ace *Get out of our way! Jack, Joker – we three Are as one in this business – do you agree?*

Joker *Aye, let's hold up our hands, swear on God's holy bones*
We'll stand up for each other till we hear Death's last groans.

Jack/Ace *Death's dead when we find him!*
Come on, let's away.

Joker *It's three on to one, Death won't win! Hurray!*

Ace *If we betray one another, may God strike us dead!*

Pardoner *As they lurched off, the innkeeper shook his head.*

Innkeeper *Fight Death? Them? Why – they can hardly stand up!*
But they're not going to listen, so I'll shut up.

Pardoner The three staggered off and walked, very slowly, all night. As the sun came up, they began to think that they must be lost.

Scene 2 In a field

Jack *Where is this village? We've walked another mile…*

Ace *Hang on, there's the way, look – over that stile.*

Old man *Good morning, good luck, God bless you all three!*
If you're not in a hurry, then come talk to me.

Joker *Oh, it's you, you old fool. Look, we don't have all day*
We're all in a hurry so get out of our way!

Old man *That's a rough way to speak to an old man like me*
Remember, one day you'll be old, you'll see.

Ace *Get lost, old man, we will never be old*
Just move along now, you must be terribly cold
Wrapped up as you are – is that your face there
Peeping out from your scarf like a wizened pear?

Jack *We've met some old men but you win first prize*
If there is anyone older, I'll be very surprised!

Old man *I'm too old it's true, but not even Death*
Will come to find me and take my last breath.

Ace *Just a minute, old man … I'll bet you're Death's spy!*
Tell us where he is!
Come on! Do not lie!

Old man *I can tell you are keen to find Death, you three*
So walk up this path to an old oak tree
That's where I left him. You'll find him, it's true
And may God who saved mankind, save you!

Pardoner *So off the three went, they thought they were smart*
But you'll see in my story, greed plays a big part!

Ace *Look, there's the oak tree! The old man was right*
Now we'll find Death so get ready to fight!

Pardoner   But the three ruffians were in for a surprise, for
it was not Death they found under the tree. At
least, not straight away...

Scene 3   At the oak tree

Jack   *I can't see Death. There's no one in sight.*

Ace   *Maybe he's seen us and he's hiding in fright.*

Joker *Forget about Death – just look what I've found*
A pile of gold florins right there on the ground!
There's no one about – I must say that's funny
It's just been left here, this great pile of money!

Jack *Whose is it? To count it, must take them hours!*

Ace *Don't be so daft! Finders keepers – it's ours!*

Joker *It's clear that we're meant to keep this treasure*
Well, we will – to spend it will be a great
pleasure!

Jack *This gold is so heavy and this path's so narrow*
To move this much gold, we'll need a
wheelbarrow!

Ace *Jack, Joker – sit down, we must have a think*
Moving money's not easy, 'cos coins clink!

Pardoner The three sat and plotted. No longer were they
just drunken fools. They were robbers too.

Jack *We must be careful moving this gold away*
People will see if we do it by day.

Ace *That's true, they will think we're a robber gang*
For taking what's ours … why, they would us
hang!

Joker *I know I'm a joker, but I've an idea*
And if we do this, we need have no fear
We'll guard this treasure, then at dead of night
We'll carry it off, keeping out of sight!

Ace *A good idea! So, let's make a plan*
We'll need food and drink … so one of us can
Go buy some in town, it's not far to hike.

Joker *Then we'll take this gold wherever we like*
By dark, share it out – three equal amounts!

Jack *We'll draw straws, and it's the longest one*
counts
Who gets it goes shopping for bread and wine
The others stand guard – there, that idea's
mine!

Joker   *Here are three straws, one is long and two short*
Come on, Jack, take one, there's no time for
thought!

Pardoner   Carefully, they each drew a straw from Joker's
hand.

Ace   *Ha! Jack's got the long straw – Joker sit down*
We'll guard the gold while Jack runs to town.

Joker   Go on, Jack, you're the youngest. Run all the way!

Jack   *I'll be back really quick, before you can say*
'He's gone!'

Ace   *He's gone! Joker, listen to me*
What's the point of sharing the gold between
three?
We can split Jack's share between us two
Every last gold florin, for me and you!

Joker *But why not? We'll do it! Er…what will Jack
say?*

Ace *Nothing at all…because…we will him…slay!*

Joker *What? How can we do that? I mean…kill Jack?*

Ace *Easy! You challenge him when he comes back
To a wrestling match, tell Jack it's just fun
But we'll both fight, two are stronger than one.*

Joker *Then in the struggle we'll each draw our dagger
And that will be that…we'll watch Jack stagger!*

Ace *With Jack dead this gold will be all ours to
spend
Shared between two, we'll take half each, dear
friend!*

19

Pardoner So the gold made Joker and Ace greedy, but Jack was greedy too, and he had an idea.

Jack *All those gold florins, new minted and bright*
If I'd found them all by myself, I might
Have had that hoard – all that gold, just for me
Just fancy not having to share between three!

I want it! I'll have it! Nothing will stop me.
The answer lies in this Chemist's shop – see,
I've got bread and wine but here is the twist
Now I'll buy poison from this old chemist!

Scene 4 At the chemist's shop

Chemist *Some poison you say...for what purpose*
please?

Jack *I've rats in my hen-run, they're covered in fleas*
So I'll poison them, and there's a wild cat too
That steals my chickens...I'll get him, wouldn't
you?

Chemist I've pondered the problem of rats till I'm weary
They carry the plague, at least that's my theory
For vermin I have a preparation
But – be warned – it will kill any man in this
    nation
Only a mouthful and they'll drop down dead
So make sure – rats only – hear what I've said?

Jack Two rats in particular come to my mind
It's just what I need, you are very kind.

Chemist All right, just wait here, I'll be back in a tick!

Jack That silly old chemist was easy to trick!
Now I'll divide up the wine into three
I'll poison two bottles – the good one's for me
And when Ace and Joker are dead and cold
I'll have bread, good wine, and all that gold!

Pardoner   *Greed, as you see, makes them plan evil deeds*
The road to ruin – that is where greed leads!

Let's now return to the tree in the wood
We'll stay a short while – they'll stay there for
good!

Scene 5   At the oak tree

Ace   *Here's Jack coming back, are you standing by?*

Joker   *I'm ready to wrestle and he's going to die*
Be there with your dagger!

Ace   *It's here, in my hand…*

Jack *Hello, you two! Well, this is just grand!*
Here are two loaves of bread and bottles of
*   wine*
These two bottles are yours, I've drunk all mine!

Pardoner *Drunkards, robbers – now murderers, all three*
And all through their greed – that is quite clear
*   to see!*

Joker *Here, Jack! Wrestling match! Just us two, for*
*   fun!*
We'll eat and drink up as soon as we've done!

Jack *All right, Joker! That will be a giggle!*

Ace *Take care, Joker, hold him, don't let him jiggle!*

Joker   *That's it. No more Jack, he's stabbed in the back.*

Ace   *Quick Joker, drag him away off the track.*

Joker   *Yes, and after that we will rest out legs*
We'll drain this wine to the very last dregs!

Pardoner   *They drank poisoned wine, so they all died in pain*
And you may well think they were all insane
Their greed for gold left all three dead
So they did meet Death as the old man said!
Remember, he told them that under the tree
They'd meet Death? It was their own death, you see!

Scene 6   At the inn

Pardoner   Now, my tale is told and my throat is so dry,
I think it's time to pay a visit to that fine and
friendly innkeeper.

Innkeeper   Ah, here's the Pardoner. I suppose you'll try to
sell me a pardon. You're wasting your time. I
don't believe in your pardons.

Pardoner   *I'll make you a deal – it's a good one – just
think
I'll pardon your sins for a long, cool drink!*

Innkeeper   *Will you really? Now, tell me, and don't take too
long
Who pardons **your** sins, when you have done
wrong?*

Pardoner   *Ah! I would like to tell you, but I've no time to
stay
Good day to you all, I'm up and away!*

Each Chaucer tale has a moral. What is the moral in *The
Pardoner's Tale?*

The Scottish Play

A Shakespearean
Mini-drama
by Stan Barrett

Illustrations by Anna C Leplar

Cast

Tim
Beth's younger
brother

Beth
a superstitious girl

**Witch 2/
Jo**

**Witch 1/
Emma**

**Witch 3/
Sam**

Fergus
a non-speaking
old man

Narrator

The Scottish Play

Narrator *We are in a village hall a few days before the Christmas pantomime 'Jack and the Beanstalk'. Outside it is dark, wet and windy. Fergus, an old man, is painting the scenery. He stops when he hears three slow, loud knocks. Beth and Tim burst through the door.*

Beth It's all right, Fergus, it's only us. Wow! It's terrible out there. Hey, Fergus! That scenery! It's brilliant!

Narrator *The old man, who never speaks, nods and smiles.*

Tim   *(Not really interested)* I suppose that's Jack's garden.

Beth   The bushes look dead real!

Tim   That's because they *are* real.

Beth   They're terrific.

Tim   Brilliant. Where's the beanstalk?

Narrator   *Fergus points to a huge plant pot, then he disappears backstage.*

Beth   You see? The beanstalk's going to grow out of that pot.

Narrator   *As Beth stares at the stage, Tim starts to search through his sister's school bag.*

Beth   *(Looking annoyed)* Hey! What are you doing in my bag?

Tim   Looking for the script.

Beth   You don't need a script. If you'd learnt your lines properly, we wouldn't need this extra rehearsal!

Tim   Ah! Here's one.

Beth   That's not it! That's 'Mac...' *(She pauses nervously)* I mean that's 'The Scottish Play'. We're doing it at school.

Tim It says here it's called 'Macbeth' and it's by William Shakespeare.

Beth *(Holding her finger to her lips)* Shhh! When you're in a theatre you never say its title. Our teacher told us.

Tim Why not? Anyway, this isn't a theatre.

Beth It is now. It's got a stage, scenery and lights, so it's a theatre. You don't say its title and you don't quote words from it. It's bad luck. Strange things can happen.

Tim I don't believe it.

Beth Well, you should.

Tim You're just superstitious. Anyway, how could you rehearse it without quoting words from it?

Beth That's different. It doesn't count when you're actually rehearsing the play.

Narrator *Beth looks at the book over Tim's shoulder. She tells him that the story is about murder and black magic. Macbeth is a warrior who wants to be king. He plans to murder the old Scottish king, then blame it on the servants.*

Tim It sounds better than 'Jack and the Beanstalk'. But look at it! I can't understand a word.

Beth *(In her grown-up's voice)* You will when you're older. That is how Shakespeare wrote in his time.

Tim What? You mean the actors all talked like this? *(Starts to read slowly in a very flat voice)* **Thrice the brinded cat hath mew'd. Thrice and once the hedge-pig whin'd.**

Narrator *They hear three slow, heavy knocks from the stage. They spin round to see Fergus. He is banging the stage floor with a brush handle. The old man glares at Tim and puts a finger to his lips. Then, he draws his finger across his throat.*

Beth It's all right, Fergus. It's just Tim. He didn't know. He won't do it again.

Narrator *Fergus stares hard at Tim. Then, shaking his head, disappears into the darkness backstage.*

Tim What was all that about?

Beth Fergus heard you quoting from 'Mac...' 'The Scottish Play', and he got upset.

Tim *(Quietly)* What a load of rubbish!

Narrator *Suddenly, there is a crash of thunder and the lights go out.*

Tim Beth! I can't see!

Beth Tim! Look at the stage!

Narrator *There is a red glow underneath the huge plant pot. By its light, three black-hooded figures gather round the pot. The thunder rumbles on.*

(The witches sound like old women, but their voices are loud and clear.)

Witch 1 Thrice the brinded cat hath mew'd.

Witch 2 Thrice and once the hedge-pig whin'd.

Witch 3 Harpier cries: 'Tis time, 'tis time.

Narrator *There is another crash of thunder. Beth and Tim clap their hands over their ears. The red glow bursts into blue and yellow flames that lick the bottom of the pot. The three figures hum softly as they circle slowly round the fire.*

Tim *(In a loud whisper)* Beth, who are they? What's happening?

Beth I can't believe this. They are the three witches from the play.

Tim What play?

Beth 'The Scottish Play'!

Tim What are they doing?

Beth Casting a spell to read Mac..., his future. Get
down and be quiet. I don't think they know
we're here.

Witch 1 Round about the cauldron go;
In the poison'd entrails throw.
Toad that under cold stone
Days and night has thirty-one
Swelter'd venom, sleeping got
Boil thou first i' th' charmed pot.

Witch 1
Witch 2 Double, double, toil and trouble;
Witch 3 Fire burn and cauldron bubble.

Narrator *The witches circle the pot still humming. Beth and Tim are sitting on the floor. They curl up and try to look as small as they can.*

Tim *(Moans)* Beth, I don't like this.

Beth It's all your fault! I told you strange things might happen!

Witch 2 Fillet of a fenny snake,
In the cauldron boil and bake;
Eye of newt, and toe of frog,
Wool of bat, and tongue of dog,
Adder's fork, and blind-worm's sting,
Lizard's leg and howlet's wing,
For a charm of pow'rful trouble,
Like a hell-broth boil and bubble.

Witch 1
Witch 2 Double, double, toil and trouble;
Witch 3 Fire burn and cauldron bubble.

Narrator *As the witches circle and hum, Tim gets over his fear and starts to creep nearer to the centre of the stage.*

Beth *(In a soft but urgent whisper)* Tim! Come back!

Tim *(In a loud whisper)* I don't think this is real. It's just somebody acting.

Narrator *The pot bubbles and spits as if it is angry. There is a deafening crash of thunder from outside that shakes the village hall. Tim scrambles back to join Beth in a huddle on the floor.*

Witch 3 Scale of dragon, tooth of wolf,
Witches' mummy, maw and gulf
Of the ravin'd salt-sea shark,
Root of hemlock digg'd i' th' dark…

Narrator *Tim crawls towards the door with Beth trying to pull him back.*

Beth *(In an urgent whisper)* Tim! Keep still. They'll see us!

Tim They've seen us already.

Beth *(Alarmed)* They're coming.

Tim I'm going!

Narrator *As they chant, two of the witches slip to the door and bar Tim's way out.*

Witch 1
Witch 2 **Double, double, toil and trouble;**
Witch 3 **Fire burn and cauldron bubble.**

Witch 2 **Cool it with a baboon's blood,**
Then the charm is firm and good.

Narrator *Tim shakes himself free of Beth. He turns to look for the fire exit. The third witch takes a branch from the stage and bars his way.*

Beth   Look out!

Narrator   *The other two witches are moving in behind him. The third witch steps closer, waves the branch at him and throws her hood back. Beth screams as she sees a horrible mask of a baby's face with a crown on its head.*

Tim   Beth! What's ... what's happening?

Witch 1
Witch 2   Listen, but speak not to 't.

Narrator   *The third witch points at Tim. She speaks to him as if he were Macbeth.*

Witch 3   **Macbeth shall not vanquish'd be until Great Birnam Wood to high Dunsinane Hill Shall come against him.**

Witch 1
Witch 2   That will never be.

Tim   Look! I don't know what you're on about and I don't care. I'm going home. Right?

Narrator   *But before Tim can move, the two witches behind him suddenly whip off their cloaks and throw them over him. Tim struggles and falls in a heap on the floor.*

Tim   *(His voice muffled)* Help! Let me out!

Narrator   *Tim stops shouting when he hears laughter. Even his sister is laughing.*

Beth *(Relieved)* Emma! Jo! And Sam! It was you all the time! And I never knew! Those voices didn't sound at all like yours.

Sam *(Proudly)* That's good acting for you.

Narrator *Tim finally gets his head free. The lights are back on and he stares at the three 'witches'. They are Beth's school friends.*

Emma Had you fooled there, didn't we?

Jo You all right, Tim? Sorry about that, but we know Beth is superstitious. We knew she'd fallen for all that bad luck stuff in 'Macbeth'.

Tim You mean it's not true?

Sam Of course it's not true. Not unless you're superstitious. Like Beth.

Beth   No, I'm not. Not really. Anyway, how come Fergus didn't stop you? He believes in it.

Emma   I know he does, but we asked him if we could rehearse the witches' scene round that big pot.

Jo   We told him it was for drama at school.

Emma   So he didn't mind. He even found us those old black curtains.

Sam   And that wicked baby mask and crown.

Emma   And he put the lights out. That's when we got the idea of trying to fool you.

Tim   I don't know why, but I got really scared when you were waving that branch at me. What was all that about?

Sam   Now, that was funny. I hadn't learnt that bit. I hadn't even looked at it, but the words just came out. It was as if something inside was telling me what to say.

Jo   Yeah. And how did we know to say: **That will never be**, at the end? That must be Macbeth's line.

Emma   *(Shrugs)* Don't know. It just came out. Strange, isn't it?

Beth   Stop it, you three. It's creepy.

Tim   But what did it mean?

Beth Well, Mac…, he wants the witches to tell him if he is safe from his enemies now he is king.

Tim So he did murder the old Scottish king?

Emma Yes, but Lady Macbeth planted the murder weapon on the servants.

Tim Lady Macbeth? Who's she?

Beth His wife. She wanted to be queen so she urged her husband to kill the old man.

Jo Mind you, she went completely mad afterwards. In her sleep she kept trying to wash the old king's blood off her hands when there was none there.

Sam And she went around saying things like: *(In an actor's voice)* **Out, damned spot!** and **Here's the smell of the blood still.**

Beth Sam! Don't!

Emma Oh, come on, Beth. You don't really believe all that stuff.

Beth Fergus does. If he hears you, he'll throw us out.

Tim *(Impatiently)* But you still haven't told me about the branch.

Emma The witches told Macbeth that he would be safe until Birnam Wood moved to the hill at Dunsinane.

Jo Macbeth thought this would never happen.

Beth But the rebel army chopped down the trees and hid behind the branches as they marched towards Dunsinane.

Sam So the forest of trees moved!

Tim Wow! What happens next?

Beth Don't tell him. Do what our teacher did. Say he's got to look at the end of the play and work it out for himself.

Tim No. Tell me now. Why should I…

Beth *(Interrupting)* Look! Look at the stage! The bushes are moving!

Narrator *They stand and stare in disbelief until they see Fergus. He is only moving the scenery round.*

Jo   Wow! That's a relief! For a minute, I thought…

Emma   Hey! I've just remembered something my mum once told me about Fergus. *(Continues quietly so that Fergus can't hear)* He used to be a stage manager in the West End.

Tim   West end of what?

Beth Oh come on, Tim. The West End of London. That's where all the big theatres are. Go on, Emma.

Emma Well, one day he said to three actresses who were playing the witches in 'Macbeth': **How now, you secret, black and midnight hags!**

Beth I wish you wouldn't do that, Emma.

Emma I have to. It's part of the story. And ever since then, he's never spoken a single word.

Jo Mind you, nobody believes it.

Sam There's more than that. They say that Fergus can speak, but only lines from 'Macbeth'. It's all a load of rubbish if you ask me.

Emma I expect you're right. Well, come on you two. We'll let Beth and Tim get on with their pantomime rehearsal.

Tim Hang on a minute! How did you manage all that thunder?

Beth Yes. And that fire under the pot? It looked so real.

Sam Thunder? What thunder?

Jo There wasn't any thunder.

Beth *(Getting cross)* Of course there was! It made the whole building shake, didn't it, Tim?

Sam There was no fire either. Just a little red light that Fergus gave us to put under the pot.

Beth *(Angrily)* Oh come on, you three! We know what we saw, don't we Tim?

Emma Beth! Just calm down a minute. I think you're winding us up to get your own back.

Tim Beth's telling the truth. We heard real thunder and saw real flames.

Emma That's weird. Really weird. I think we should go. All of us. Right now, before anything else happens.

Tim But we haven't rehearsed our scene in 'Jack' yet.

Beth We'll do it at home. *(Loudly)* Cheers, Fergus. And thanks for letting us in.

Narrator Fergus waves to the children as they go. He stands on the stage and stares into space. He is startled by three slow, loud bangs and three dark, shadowy shapes as they gather round the pot. He speaks: **How now, you secret, black and midnight hags!**

What have you learnt about the story of 'Macbeth' from this play?

Glossary

adder's fork   forked tongue of an adder

blind-worm   slow-worm (used to be thought poisonous)

brinded   striped, like a tabby cat

cauldron   a large pot placed over a fire

entrails   the insides of a body

fenny snake   a snake that comes from the wet, swampy part of England called the Fens

fillet   a slice of meat

gulf   throat

hags   ugly old women, especially witches

harpier   an evil being

hath   has

hedge-pig   hedgehog

hell-broth   a soup made in Hell

hemlock   a poisonous plant

howlet   a baby owl

maw	stomach
mew'd	the sound made by a cat
ravin'd	extremely hungry
sleeping got	caught while asleep
swelter'd	hot and sweaty
thrice	three times
toil	hard, difficult work
vanquish'd	beaten in a battle
venom	poison
whin'd	a long, complaining sound
witches' mummy	dried flesh used by witches as medicine

The Curse of the Baskervilles

*A Classic
Detective Story
Adapted by Angela Lanyon*

Illustrations by Linda Clark

Cast

Narrator

Dr Watson
Holmes's assistant

Sherlock Holmes
the famous
detective

Mrs Barrymore
Baskerville Hall's
housekeeper

Mr Stapleton
Henrietta Baskerville's
neighbour

Henrietta Baskerville
The owner of Baskerville Hall

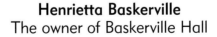

The Curse of the Baskervilles

Scene 1   *Inside Sherlock Holmes' flat*

Narrator   *Sherlock Holmes, the famous detective, lives in London. He and Dr Watson, his assistant, are having breakfast in their flat in Baker Street. There is a knock at the door and Henrietta Baskerville enters.*

Henrietta   Mr Holmes? I need help. I have just arrived from America and found this letter waiting for me at my hotel.

Holmes   Read it out, Watson.

Dr Watson   'If you value your life, stay away from Baskerville Hall.' What does it mean?

Henrietta   My uncle has just died. I didn't even know him but he has left me his house, Baskerville Hall. It's a great big old house in Devon.

Holmes   How did your uncle die?

Henrietta   He'd gone into the garden last thing at night and when he didn't return, the housekeeper went to look for him. She found him lying dead on the path.

Dr Watson   Did he have a heart attack?

Henrietta   Not exactly. That's what makes it so spooky. His face was a mask of terror. It looked as though he had died of fear!

Holmes   Baskerville Hall is in the middle of Dartmoor.

Watson   It must be close to Dartmoor prison.

Holmes   Ah, a prisoner escaped from Dartmoor prison yesterday. Perhaps that is connected with the letter in some way.

Henrietta Mr Sherlock Holmes, I have heard you are the best detective in the country. Will you find out who sent the letter? Am I really in danger?

Narrator *Holmes leans forward, his face keen with interest.*

Holmes Yes, I will. Watson, you must go to Devon and guard Miss Baskerville. I have work to do.

Scene 2 *That evening in the drawing room of Baskerville Hall*

Narrator *Henrietta and Watson are now at Baskerville Hall. It is late in the evening and Henrietta is reading.*

Henrietta I'm reading about local legends. There are some ghost stories which local people believe are true! I shall be afraid to set foot out of doors.

Dr Watson The moor will look brighter in daylight.

Narrator *The housekeeper enters.*

Mrs Barrymore Mr Stapleton is here to see you.

Dr Watson Mr Stapleton is our nearest neighbour, I believe. He lives in the cottage you see from the window.

Narrator *Mr Stapleton enters.*

Mr Stapleton Miss Baskerville, welcome to Dartmoor.
I know it's late but as soon as I saw your
lights on, I decided to call in.

Henrietta That's mighty kind. Meet my friend
Dr Watson.

Mr Stapleton An honour, sir.

Narrator *Suddenly, a distant howling breaks the silence.*

Dr Watson Whatever's that?

Henrietta It sounded like a wild dog.

Mrs Barrymore It's the curse of the Baskervilles. I heard it the night your uncle died.

Henrietta Whatever do you mean? Are you making this up?

Mrs Barrymore No miss, it's true as I stand here.

Dr Watson Well then, out with it. Tell us the story.

Mrs Barrymore That picture over the fireplace, that's the wicked Sir Charles, one of the oldest Baskervilles.

Mr Stapleton He lived here three hundred years ago.

Mrs Barrymore He treated his wife cruelly until she could stand it no longer. One night she ran off and escaped across the moor.

Dr Watson Poor woman!

Mrs Barrymore He went after her with his hounds. They chased her into Great Grimpen Swamp and she was sucked down.

Mr Stapleton The swamp is a very dangerous place.

Mrs Barrymore She cursed him, she did. Called on the devil to take him.

Henrietta What happened?

Mrs Barrymore Before the night was over, a huge hound tore out his throat. It was a giant hound and it gleamed with a strange white light.

Dr Watson How frightful!

Mrs Barrymore The ghost hound still haunts the Baskervilles.

Henrietta How do you know?

Mrs Barrymore Beside your uncle's body, in the earth of the flower bed, there were the footprints of a gigantic hound!

Scene 3 *The next morning in Stapleton Cottage*

Narrator *The next day, Henrietta and Dr Watson are visiting Mr Stapleton's cottage. The sun is shining.*

Mr Stapleton I must warn you about keeping to the paths. Great Grimpen Swamp has sucked many walkers to their death.

Dr Watson I expect that's what happened to the prisoner. No one's seen him.

Narrator *Henrietta laughs out loud.*

Henrietta Maybe the ghost hound got him.

Mr Stapleton You shouldn't laugh. Your uncle believed the story.

Henrietta   Yes, but I've got more sense, Mr Stapleton. Come, Dr Watson, let's continue our walk.

Narrator   *Across the moor, a figure is seen hurrying away.*

Henrietta   Gee! Who's that?

Dr Watson   The escaped prisoner I imagine. He's making for that hut. I'll go after him.

Narrator   *A shadow falls across the door. Sherlock Holmes stands in the doorway…*

Dr Watson   Holmes, what on earth are you doing here?

Holmes   Watson, we are approaching the heart of the mystery. Remind me what we have discovered so far.

Dr Watson   We know that Henrietta got a letter warning her to keep away from Baskerville Hall, if she values her life. We know there is an escaped prisoner about. And Mrs Barry, the housekeeper, believes that Henrietta's uncle was frightened to death by a ghostly hound.

Holmes   So who sent the mysterious letter? I am not the escaped prisoner, so where is he? And the vital question, Watson, does this ghostly hound exist?

Dr Watson   But you don't believe in ghosts, Holmes.

Holmes   Exactly! Miss Baskerville is in deadly danger. We must move fast if we're to save her. I'll join you at the Hall tonight.

Scene 4   ***That afternoon in Baskerville Hall***

Narrator   *Baskerville Hall in the late afternoon. Outside there is thick mist and Henrietta is cross.*

Henrietta   I don't believe it. I hung my big cloak in the lobby and now it's vanished.

Dr Watson   Are you sure?

Henrietta   Yes, I've looked everywhere.

Dr Watson   Maybe Mrs Barrymore has hung it to dry somewhere.

Narrator   *Mrs Barrymore enters. Her eyes are red and she looks as if she has been crying. She twists her hands.*

Mrs Barrymore   Excuse me, Miss, a message came when you were out. Mr Holmes will be here this evening.

Henrietta That's great. Maybe he can find my cloak.

Mrs Barrymore Your green cloak, Miss? I haven't seen it.

Henrietta How do you know it's green if you haven't seen it?

Narrator *Mrs Barrymore looks confused and stammers.*

Mrs Barrymore You must have been wearing it when you arrived here.

Narrator *Mrs Barrymore hurries away.*

Dr Watson That woman's lying.

Henrietta When Mr Holmes arrives he'll get to the bottom of all this.

Scene 5 ***That evening in the drawing room of Baskerville Hall***

Narrator *Later in the same evening, Holmes and Dr Watson are sitting by the fire in Baskerville Hall. Outside the wind is blustering.*

Holmes Watson, did you see that?

Dr Watson See what?

Holmes A flash of light outside. I think it's coming from inside the house.

Narrator *Holmes springs to his feet and dashes from the room. Dr Watson follows him. The house is in darkness but there is a faint light on the landing. Racing up the stairs they find Mrs Barrymore standing at a window. She has a torch and is moving it backwards and forwards. Holmes seizes her wrist.*

Holmes Stop!

Mrs Barrymore I wasn't doing anything.

Holmes   You were signalling. Look!

Narrator   *Across the moor, a distant light shows. It goes on and off at regular intervals.*

Watson   Could it be the ghost hound?

Holmes   Nonsense, Watson. It's coming from the hut.

Mrs Barrymore   No, it's my brother, Mr Holmes. He's hiding out on the moor.

Dr Watson   You mean your brother is the escaped prisoner.

Mrs Barrymore   Yes. He was led into bad company and I always felt he was falsely imprisoned. I couldn't leave him to go hungry and cold.

Holmes   So that's where Miss Baskerville's green cloak went. You stole it for your brother!

Mrs Barrymore   Oh, give him a chance, sir, don't let him be found.

Dr Watson   The police must hear of this. The telephone exchange is shut now. I'll call them tomorrow.

Scene 6   ***The next morning on the moor near Great Grimpen Swamp***

Narrator   *On the following morning Holmes and Dr Watson are walking along the edge of Great Grimpen Swamp. A long drawn-out howl echoes across the moor.*

Dr Watson Good Heavens, Holmes, what's that? Is it the ghost hound?

Holmes Not a ghost hound, Watson, but a creature of flesh and blood. It's hiding somewhere in the swamp.

Narrator *Dr Watson strides forward but Holmes pulls him back.*

Holmes It will be certain death, my friend, if you wander into the swamp.

Dr Watson   I think someone must be going in there to feed the hound.

Holmes   Yes, someone who knows the paths.

Dr Watson   Who would want to feed a dog like that?

Narrator   *Suddenly, something catches Watson's eye.*

Dr Watson   Look, Holmes, over there! Who's that?

Narrator   *A figure in a long cloak is being chased by a huge hound. The hound jumps on the figure.*

Holmes   We are too late, Watson.

Narrator   *Suddenly, they hear a shrill whistle. The dog runs off into the moor.*

Dr Watson Holmes, did you hear that? We're right, there is someone looking after the hound.

Narrator *The figure is lying on the ground.*

Holmes Quick, in case there is any sign of life.

Dr Watson Do you think it's Miss Baskerville?

Narrator *Approaching the figure, they turn it over.*

Holmes It is Mrs Barrymore's brother if I am not mistaken. He's dead.

Narrator *Mr Stapleton runs out of his cottage.*

Mr Stapleton What's happened – I heard cries. Did I see Miss Baskerville go by? Is she all right?

Holmes Save your pity, Mr Stapleton, this is not Miss Baskerville but the escaped prisoner. The poor fellow would have been safer staying in prison than wandering out here.

Mr Stapleton But what killed him?

Holmes The curse of the Baskervilles, Mr Stapleton. A gigantic hound.

Scene 7 ***The next day outside Stapleton Cottage***

Narrator *Later the following day a thick mist is drifting down from the hilltops. A gloomy silence covers the moor. Henrietta and Mr Stapleton are outside his cottage. Holmes and Dr Watson are hiding in the heather.*

Holmes Careful, Watson. We must get close enough to hear what they are saying. Have you your revolver?

Dr Watson In my pocket, Holmes.

Narrator *They crawl closer and Holmes puts his finger to his lips.*

Henrietta When I say 'no' Mr Stapleton, I mean no.

Mr Stapleton From the moment I first saw you, Henrietta…

Henrietta Don't think you can force me into marrying you.

Mr Stapleton   But I love you, Henrietta. Say you will?

Henrietta   I've just told you 'no'. And don't imagine you'll talk me into it. I'm spoken for. There is a young man back in America. Why, we're practically engaged.

Mr Stapleton   Then I've nothing more to say. But remember the curse of the Baskervilles.

Henrietta   Are you trying to frighten me with ghost stories? Shame on you.

Mr Stapleton   Your uncle believed them.

Henrietta   He wasn't an American.

Narrator   *Henrietta starts off down the path. Holmes and Watson creep out of hiding and follow Henrietta.*

Holmes   Curse this mist. It's getting thicker.

Dr Watson   We shall lose sight of her before long.

Narrator   *They hear a howling. Henrietta turns, then starts to run.*

Holmes   Quick, Watson, your revolver.

Narrator   *As he speaks a great hound bursts from the mist, its tongue hangs out and saliva drips from its muzzle. Its head and body gleam with an eerie white light. It leaps towards Henrietta.*

Holmes   Shoot, Watson, shoot!

Narrator   *Dr Watson fires his revolver and the beast drops in the middle of its spring.*

Henrietta   What in the world…?

Holmes   A vicious creature, Miss Baskerville. This is no ghost but a real dog covered with shining white paint.

Dr Watson   So this is what scared your poor uncle to death!

Holmes   And now for the villain who is behind all this – Mr Stapleton.

Henrietta   But he's just this minute asked me to marry him.

Holmes   And if you'd agreed you'd have been safe. Hadn't you noticed, Watson, how alike he and Miss Baskerville are?

Watson   Now you mention it, they do look alike.

Holmes   You were your uncle's long lost niece… but he didn't know he also had a nephew. That nephew is Mr Stapleton. And he felt the estate should belong to him. Your uncle's will clearly states that the house now belongs to you, but Mr Stapleton would be the next in line to inherit. So he used the dog to frighten your uncle to death. Then he tried it again – or worse.

Narrator   *Mr Stapleton comes out of his cottage.*

Mr Stapleton   I heard a shot! Is Miss Baskerville all right?

Henrietta   I'm fine, Mr Stapleton. But Mr Holmes has just told me what you were planning to do.

Mr Stapleton But Henrietta…

Holmes I think you've got some questions to answer.

Mr Stapleton No! No! I know nothing about the hound.

Narrator *Holmes steps forward to take Mr Stapleton's arm but he brushes him off.*

Mr Stapleton You'll not take me. Never.

Narrator *Turning on his heels, he runs towards Great Grimpen Swamp. The mist swirls round him and he slips. He overbalances and with a long scream he falls into the swamp.*

Dr Watson Holmes, quick, we must save him.

Holmes There's nothing we can do. By the time we reach him he'll have vanished.

Narrator *As the green and muddy waters of the swamp close over his head, a last shrill cry echoes across the moor. Mr Stapleton has disappeared for ever.*

Dr Watson Holmes – how did you know it was a real hound?

Holmes Elementary, my dear Watson. Phantom dogs don't leave footprints behind them!

What clues led Sherlock Holmes to suspect Mr Stapleton?